Would You Rather

Family Game Book for Kids
6–12 Years Old

Book 1

Kabukuma Kids

ISBN: 978-1-952758-02-7

www.kabukuma.com

Connect with Kabukuma

▶ youtube.com/kabukuma

instagram.com/kabukuma

f facebook.com/kabukuma

Share a book selfie and tag
#Kabukuma

Email a book selfie to Kabukuma:
kabukuma@kabukuma.com

This book belongs to:

_____

Categories

How to Play

Home

School

Animals

Food

Games

Media

Fantasy

How to Play

Invite a friend or family member to play with you. The more the merrier. Take turns answering questions. Encourage players to explain their answers.
Have fun!

Would You Rather is a fun game to play:

- at parties,
- at sleepovers,
- on a rainy day,
- in the car or on a plane,
- to unplug from the internet,
- to develop good listening skills,
- to express your ideas,
- to learn about one another,
- to laugh and smile.

HOME

WOULD YOU RATHER

give up WiFi for one week
OR
give up video games for one week?

take out the trash
OR
walk the dog?

WOULD YOU RATHER

never fix your bed again
OR
never brush your teeth again?

stay up late
OR
sleep in late?

WOULD YOU RATHER

live in a mansion in the city
OR
in a barn on a farm?

have a pet lizard
OR
a pet snake?

WOULD YOU RATHER

clean the entire house
OR
never take a bath again?

have a personal chef
OR
a personal house cleaner?

WOULD YOU RATHER

live in a tree house
OR
live on a houseboat?

have a swimming pool
OR
a trampoline in your backyard?

WOULD YOU RATHER

share all your toys with your sibling
OR
own one toy you never have to
share?

have twin brothers
OR
twin sisters?

WOULD YOU RATHER

switch places with your mom
OR
switch places with your dad?

switch places with your sibling
OR
switch places with your pet?

WOULD YOU RATHER

own an amusement park
OR
own a video game arcade?

sleep with a security blanket
OR
sleep with a teddy bear?

WOULD YOU RATHER

go back in time when you were a
baby
OR
go to your future as an adult?

have a grandma who raps
OR
a mom who breakdances?

WOULD YOU RATHER

have a robot butler
OR
a virtual reality headset?

have a magic oven that bakes
anything you want to eat
OR
a self-driving car that drives you
anywhere you want to go?

SCHOOL

WOULD YOU RATHER

be the school principal for a day
OR
be the teacher for a day?

go to school early and leave early
OR
go to school late and leave late?

WOULD YOU RATHER

go to the museum on a field trip
OR
go to the zoo on a field trip?

wear a clown nose to school
OR
wear a fake mustache to school?

WOULD YOU RATHER

sit in the front of the class
OR
sit in the back of the class?

be the class president
OR
the teacher's pet?

WOULD YOU RATHER

sing in the talent show
OR
dance in the talent show?

do a one page oral report in class
OR
a 5 page written report in class?

WOULD YOU RATHER

paint during art class
OR
play soccer during PE class?

sing in the school chorus
OR
play trumpet in the school band?

WOULD YOU RATHER

have a pet lizard in the classroom
OR
a pet turtle in the classroom?

bring your sibling to class
OR
bring your pet to class?

WOULD YOU RATHER

work in the school cafeteria
OR
work in the school library?

be a speed reader
OR
a math whiz?

WOULD YOU RATHER

have a strict teacher who teaches you a lot
OR
an easy teacher who teaches you very little?

be the top student in school
OR
the top athlete in school?

WOULD YOU RATHER

go on vacation with homework
OR
stay home with no homework?

earn a perfect score on your
math test
OR
earn a perfect score on your
spelling test?

WOULD YOU RATHER

attend an ice cream party at your school
OR
attend movie night at your school?

be driven to school in a limousine
OR
parachute to school from an airplane?

ANIMALS

WOULD YOU RATHER

have tentacles for arms
OR
a fishtail for feet?

be an earthworm who lives in the
dirt
OR
a crab who lives in the sand?

ANIMALS

WOULD YOU RATHER

have tentacles for arms
OR
a fishtail for feet?

be an earthworm who lives in the
dirt
OR
a crab who lives in the sand?

WOULD YOU RATHER

be the ruler of the jungle
OR
the ruler of the sea?

visit an aquarium
OR
visit a zoo?

WOULD YOU RATHER

be a venomous cobra snake
OR
a poisonous pufferfish?

have six legs
OR
insect antennae on your head?

WOULD YOU RATHER

ride a camel in the desert
OR
ride an elephant in the jungle?

be a peacock with vibrant feathers
OR
a monarch butterfly with vibrant
wings?

WOULD YOU RATHER

be raised by a tribe of monkeys
OR
raised by a pack of wolves?

switch places with a dog
OR
switch places with a cat?

WOULD YOU RATHER

have good hearing like a bat
OR
a good sense of smell like a
bloodhound?

smell stinky like a skunk
OR
eat garbage like a raccoon?

WOULD YOU RATHER

be a nocturnal animal like a
night owl
OR
a diurnal animal like a day squirrel?

fly like an eagle
OR
swim like a shark?

WOULD YOU RATHER

live with beavers in a dam
OR
live with horses in a stable?

be a talking parrot
OR
a flying squirrel?

WOULD YOU RATHER

be a frog that eats flies
OR
a bat that eats mosquitoes?

be a dinosaur living in the
prehistoric world
OR
a cockroach living 100 years in the
future?

WOULD YOU RATHER

be a dog who surfs on the beach
OR
a dog who sled races in the snow?

be an ugly duckling who becomes a
swan
OR
a caterpillar who becomes a
butterfly?

FOOD

WOULD YOU RATHER

enter a hot dog eating contest
OR
enter a pie eating contest?

wear a hot dog costume on
Halloween
OR
wear a hamburger costume on
Halloween?

WOULD YOU RATHER

swim in a sea of chocolate
OR
live in a gingerbread house?

eat cupcakes on your birthday
OR
eat donuts on your birthday?

WOULD YOU RATHER

eat peanut butter and jelly
sandwiches for a week
OR
eat grilled cheese sandwiches for
a week?

eat a plate of broccoli
OR
eat a plate of cauliflower?

WOULD YOU RATHER

have meatless Mondays
OR
spinach Sundays?

eat tacos on Tuesdays
OR
eat sushi on Saturdays?

WOULD YOU RATHER

give up chicken nuggets forever
OR
give up pizza forever?

eat fried frog legs
OR
eat snails sautéed in butter?

WOULD YOU RATHER

work in an ice cream shop
OR
work in a candy shop?

snack on popcorn at the movies
OR
snack on nachos at the movies?

WOULD YOU RATHER

eat breakfast on a pirate ship
OR
eat dinner in a royal castle?

eat a sour lemon
OR
eat a spicy pepper?

WOULD YOU RATHER

eat a cockroach if you were stuck
on a desert island
OR
eat a snake if you were stuck
on a desert island?

eat steak for breakfast
OR
eat pancakes for dinner?

WOULD YOU RATHER

drink a milkshake out of a
baby bottle
OR
sip an ice cream sundae through
a straw?

win a year's supply of candy
OR
win a year's supply of pizza?

WOULD YOU RATHER

bring a werewolf home for dinner
OR
bring a vampire home for dinner?

be a famous chef with your own TV
show
OR
be a famous baker with your own
bakery?

GAMES

WOULD YOU RATHER

play volleyball against a kangaroo
OR
play volleyball against a seal?

run a race against a rabbit
OR
run a race against a llama?

WOULD YOU RATHER

build a sandcastle at the beach
OR
build a snowman in the winter?

ice skate
OR
rollerblade?

WOULD YOU RATHER

kick the winning goal in soccer
OR
be the goalie who blocks the
winning goal?

sing the national anthem before a
soccer game
OR
sing Take Me Out to the Ballgame
at the baseball game?

WOULD YOU RATHER

play chess against an alien
OR
play checkers against a zombie?

play Hide and Seek with elves
OR
play dodgeball against a giant?

WOULD YOU RATHER

design a new video game
OR
invent a new sport?

play on an Esports team with your
family
OR
play on an Esports team against
your friends?

WOULD YOU RATHER

play a single player video game alone
OR
play a board game with a group of friends?

fly a kite
OR
fly a drone?

WOULD YOU RATHER

go fishing on the sea
OR
snowboarding in the mountains?

go bungee jumping
OR
go skydiving?

WOULD YOU RATHER

be the top scoring player on a
losing team
OR
the lowest scoring player on a
winning team?

be a famous athlete
OR
a video game designer?

WOULD YOU RATHER

attend a pro basketball game
OR
attend a pro hockey game?

wear an alligator costume as the
team mascot
OR
wear a bear costume as the team
mascot?

WOULD YOU RATHER

win a million dollars in the lottery
OR
win an Olympic gold medal?

win all the slime in the world
OR
win all the stickers in the world?

MEDIA

WOULD YOU RATHER

unplug from the internet for one
week
OR
not speak a word for one week?

communicate using only text emojis
OR
communicate using only a pen and
paper?

WOULD YOU RATHER

take dance lessons from a
K-Pop star
OR
singing lessons from a country star?

go to a movie premier
in a limousine
OR
attend a music concert with a
backstage pass?

WOULD YOU RATHER

sing a pop song in karaoke
OR
rap a hip hop song in karaoke?

be a Youtube star
OR
a TikTok star?

WOULD YOU RATHER

be the superhero in an action movie
OR
the villain in an action movie?

watch a scary movie that gives you
nightmares
OR
listen to a song that gets stuck in
your head?

WOULD YOU RATHER

live in a library for one year
OR
live in a movie theater for one year?

paint an artwork that hangs in a
museum
OR
conduct an orchestra?

WOULD YOU RATHER

give up your computer for one week
OR
give up your mobile phone for one
week?

be a contestant on a game show
OR
be the host of a talk show?

WOULD YOU RATHER

direct a blockbuster movie
OR
write a bestselling novel?

read a book that makes you laugh
OR
watch a movie that makes you cry?

WOULD YOU RATHER

play the drums in a rock band
OR
sing in a champion a cappella
group?

give up listening to music for one
month
OR
give up watching movies for one
year?

WOULD YOU RATHER

go to the school of rock
OR
go to Youtube camp?

be a cartoon character in an
animated movie
OR
the star of a Broadway musical?

WOULD YOU RATHER

win a million dollars in the lottery
OR
be the star of a viral video with a
million views?

create an internet meme starring
your grandma
OR
teach your mom a TikTok dance?

FANTASY

WOULD YOU RATHER

have a vampire as your teacher
OR
a werewolf as your teacher?

be a pirate with a treasure chest
OR
a wizard with a book of spells?

WOULD YOU RATHER

have the power to talk to animals
OR
the power to morph into any
animal?

be turned into a frog by an
evil witch
OR
be turned into a mouse by an
evil witch?

WOULD YOU RATHER

live on a planet covered in
cotton candy
OR
live on a planet covered in slime?

be a Leprechaun with a pot of gold
OR
an ogre who lives in a royal castle?

WOULD YOU RATHER

breathe fire like a dragon
OR
see into the future like a wizard?

travel back in time 100 years
OR
travel 100 years into the future?

WOULD YOU RATHER

have the power to fly
OR
the power to be invisible?

grant your best friend three wishes
OR
a genie grant you a single wish?

WOULD YOU RATHER

live in a shack under a rainbow
OR
live in a castle under a storm cloud?

have an elf for a brother
OR
a fairy for a sister?

WOULD YOU RATHER

sprinkle fairy dust that makes
people fall asleep
OR
sprinkle fairy dust that makes
people fall in love?

have a mermaid tail for feet
OR
a unicorn horn on your head?

WOULD YOU RATHER

meet an alien in outer space
OR
meet a mermaid under the sea?

adopt a pet dragon
OR
adopt a pet unicorn?

WOULD YOU RATHER

discover your mom is a witch
OR
discover your dad is a werewolf?

inherit a magic wand that makes
things disappear
OR
inherit a magic wand that makes
things appear?

WOULD YOU RATHER

work in a toy factory with elves
OR
travel to Mars with aliens?

befriend a unicorn that
poops candy
OR
befriend a pirate who discovers
buried treasure in your backyard?

Finished Reading

Check off the chapters you have read

- ☐ Home
- ☐ School
- ☐ Animals
- ☐ Food
- ☐ Games
- ☐ Media
- ☐ Fantasy

Good Job!

Books by Kabukuma

kabukuma.com/books

Would You Rather: Family Game Book for Kids
6-12 Years Old, Book 2

Toddler Coloring Book 123
Learn to Count Numbers: A Fun Math
Preschool Workbook

Toddler Activity Book 123
Learn to Count Numbers: A Fun Math
Preschool Workbook

Join the

Kabukuma Kids Club

FREE bonus printables for
Would You Rather Book 1 readers.

Link below:

https://bit.ly/book1bonus

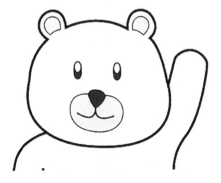

A Note from Kabukuma

Thank you beary much for playing Would You Rather with me! I hope this game made you laugh and wonder about your favorite animals, foods, and activities.

My favorite type of game is a game you can play with the whole family or with a group of friends. What games do you like?

Kabukuma started in 2012 as a YouTube channel with craft tutorials for kids. Now, I am sharing my love of games through activity books.

If you liked Would You Rather Book 1, check out Would You Rather Book 2. If you enjoyed reading this book please take the time to write a review. Your review will help me create better books that everyone can enjoy.
Hearing from my readers just makes me feel so warm and fuzzy!

See you next time!

Kabukuma

Acknowledgement

Kabukuma sends a bear hug and a big thank you to:

Ty and Reese Marumoto
Era and Ellis Hoey
Mila Elliott

for their helpful feedback at the start of writing this book.

Kabukuma wants to thank you, the reader, for playing in the world of Kabukuma.
Be sure to check out my craft tutorials on YouTube for more fun activities.

I hope you'll continue to read my books and explore the Kabukuma universe with me.
I have many hobbies like drawing, sports and stargazing that I'd love to share with you.

Connect with Kabukuma

YouTube:
youtube.com/Kabukuma

Facebook:
facebook.com/Kabukuma

Instagram:
instagram.com/kabukuma

Email:
kabukuma@kabukuma.com

Share a photo of a book selfie or a photo of your activity or coloring page and tag Kabukuma on social media.

#kabukuma

I'd love to see your beautiful work!

Bonus Puzzle

Fill in the missing letters

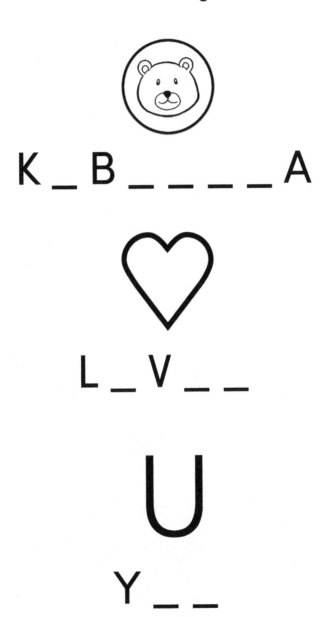

K _ B _ _ _ _ A

L _ V _ _

Y _ _

Made in the USA
Middletown, DE
07 December 2020

26784509R00060